Step by

Anti-Inflammatory

Diet Cookbook

Easy Guide with Delicious Recipes, a
Simple Way to Purifying Your Body While
Losing Weight and Increasing Energy

Susie Kessler

Table of Contents

Introduction

Most of the widely consumed diets incorporate anti-inflammation diet principles. In particular, the Mediterranean diet has whole grains, fish, and fats that are beneficial for the heart. Studies suggest that this diet can help lower the effects of cardiovascular system inflammation due to diet. Taking an anti-inflammatory diet is can be a complementary therapy for most conditions that are aggravated by chronic inflammation.

An anti-inflammation diet entails eating only particular kinds of food and avoiding others to lower the symptoms of chronic inflammatory diseases. It is one of the recommended measures that an individual can take to reduce or prevent inflammation induced by diet.

Expectedly, an anti-inflammatory diet involves nutrient-dense plant foods and minimizing or avoiding processed meats and foods. The goal of an anti-inflammation diet is to minimize inflammatory responses. The diet entails substituting refined foods with whole and nutrient-laden foods. Predictably, an anti-inflammation diet will contain more amounts of antioxidants that are reactive molecules in food and help reduce the number of free radicals. The free radicals are molecules in the human body that may harm cells and enhance the risk of certain diseases.

In particular, an anti-inflammation diet can help with the following diseases/conditions:

- Diabetes

Focusing exclusively on type 2 diabetes arises when the body fails to properly utilize insulin leading to higher than normal blood sugar levels. The condition of more sugar levels in the blood than normal is also known as hyperglycemia. It is also called insulin resistance. At the beginning of type 2 diabetes, the pancreas tries to make more insulin but fails to catch up with the rising blood sugar levels.

- Inflammatory bowel disease

Inflammatory bowel disease is a common gastrointestinal disorder that affects the large intestine. The symptoms of inflammatory bowel disease include abdominal pain, cramping, bloating, constipation, and diarrhea. It is a chronic condition, and it has to be managed in the long-term. Dietary measures are necessary to prevent diet-induced bloating, abdominal pain, diarrhea, and constipation. However, only a small percentage of individuals with inflammatory bowel disease will have extreme symptoms manifestation.

· Obesity

Medically, obesity refers to a complex disorder involving excessive amounts of body fat. Expectedly, obesity increases the risk of heart diseases as well as other health problems. Fortunately, modest weight loss can help halt and reverse the effects of obesity. Dietary adjustments can help address the causes of obesity, and the anti-inflammatory diet is inherently a healthy diet.

· Heart disease

Cardiovascular diseases can be triggered by diet, and diet can is used to manage several heart diseases. Food-related factors that increase the risk of heart diseases include obesity and high blood pressure. The type of fat eaten can also worsen or lesser risk of developing heart disease. In particular, cholesterol, saturated and trans fats are thought to increase heart attack rates. Most obese individuals also tend to have high-fat diets.

- Metabolic syndrome

Medically, metabolic syndrome refers to a group of factors that manifest together, leading to an increase in the risk of developing other inflammatory conditions. Some of these conditions include high blood pressure, excess body fat, especially around the waist, abnormal cholesterol, and high blood sugar levels. Having any or all of these conditions signifies that you are at a higher risk of developing a chronic condition. Most of these conditions are also associated with consuming an inflammation diet.

- Hashimoto's disease

Hashimoto's disease is an autoimmune disorder in which the body attacks its own tissues and, in particular, the thyroid organ. The result of unmanaged Hashimoto's disease is hypothyroidism implying that the body will not make adequate hormones. The thyroid gland makes hormones that control body metabolism, which includes heart rate and calories utilization. Unchecked Hashimoto's disease will also result in difficulties in swallowing when goiter manifests. Diet adjustments can be used to help manage the disease along with medications.

- Lupus

Lupus is another autoimmune disease that occurs when the body attacks its own organs and tissues. The inflammation occasioned by unmanaged lupus will affect other parts of the body. For instance, inflammation triggered by lupus will affect the heart, lungs, kidneys, and skin, including the brain and blood cells. The common symptoms of lupus are fever, fatigue, chest pain, dry eyes, and butterfly-shaped rash. Diet can be used to minimize the worsening of inflammation by adhering to the anti-inflammatory diet.

The other benefit of taking an anti-inflammation diet is that it can help lower the risk of select cancers such as colorectal cancer.

Grilled Salmon with Caponata

Preparation Time: 15 minutes

Cooking Time: 20 minutes

Servings: 4

Ingredients:

1. ¼ cup good-quality olive oil, divided
2. 1 onion, chopped
3. 2 celery stalks, chopped
4. 1 tablespoon minced garlic
5. 2 tomatoes, chopped
6. ½ cup chopped marinated artichoke hearts
7. ¼ cup pitted green olives, chopped
8. ¼ cup cider vinegar
9. 2 tablespoons white wine
10. 2 tablespoons chopped pecans
11. 4 (4-ounce) salmon fillets
12. Freshly ground black pepper, for seasoning
13. 2 tablespoons chopped fresh basil

- **Directions:**

  Make the caponata. In a large skillet at medium heat, warm 3 tablespoons of the olive oil. Add the onion, celery, garlic, and sauté until they have softened, about 4 minutes. Stir in the tomatoes, artichoke hearts, olives, vinegar, white wine, and pecans. Place the mixture to a boil, then reduce the heat to low and simmer until the liquid has reduced, 6 to 7 minutes. Take off the skillet from the heat and set it aside.

- Grill the fish. Preheat a grill to medium-high heat. Pat the fish dry using paper towels then rub it with the remaining 1 tablespoon of olive oil and season lightly with black pepper. Grill the salmon, turning once, until it is just cooked through, about 8 minutes total.

- Serve. Divide the salmon between four plates, top with a generous scoop of the caponata, and serve immediately with fresh basil.

Nutrition:

Calories: 348

Total fat: 25g

Total carbs: 7g

Fiber: 3g

Net carbs: 4g

Sodium: 128mg

Protein: 24g

Sweet Crab Cakes

Preparation Time: 15 minutes

Cooking Time: 10 minutes

Servings: 4

Ingredients:

1. 1 pound cooked lump crabmeat, drained and picked over
2. ¼ cup shredded unsweetened coconut
3. 1 tablespoon Dijon mustard
4. 1 scallion, finely chopped
5. ¼ cup minced red bell pepper
6. 1 egg, lightly beaten
7. 1 teaspoon lemon zest

8. Pinch cayenne pepper

9. 3 tablespoons coconut flour

10.   3 tablespoons coconut oil

11.   ¼ cup Classic Aioli

Directions:

- Make the crab cakes. In a medium bowl, mix the crab, coconut, mustard, scallion, red bell pepper, egg, lemon zest, and cayenne until it holds together. Form the mixture into eight equal patties about ¾ inch thick.

- Chill. Place the patties on a plate, cover the plate with plastic wrap, and chill them in the refrigerator for around 1 hour to 12 hours.

- Coat the patties. Spread the coconut flour on a plate. Dip each patty in the flour until it is lightly coated.

- Cook. In a large skillet at medium heat, warm the coconut oil. Fry the crab-cake patties, turning them once, until they are golden and cooked through, about 5 minutes per side.

- Serve. Place two crab cakes on each of four plates and serve with the aioli.

Nutrition:

Calories: 370

Total fat: 24g

Total carbs: 12g

 Fiber: 6g

Net carbs: 6g

Sodium: 652mg

 Protein: 26g

Herbed Coconut Milk Steamed Mussels

Preparation Time: 10 minutes

Cooking Time: 15 minutes

Servings: 4

Ingredients:

1. 2 tablespoons coconut oil
2. ½ sweet onion, chopped
3. 2 teaspoons minced garlic
4. 1 teaspoon grated fresh ginger
5. ½ teaspoon turmeric
6. 1 cup coconut milk
7. Juice of 1 lime
8. 1½ pounds fresh mussels, scrubbed and debearded
9. 1 scallion, finely chopped
10. 2 tablespoons chopped fresh cilantro
11. 1 tablespoon chopped fresh thyme

Directions:

- Sauté the aromatics. In a huge skillet, warm the coconut oil. Add the onion, garlic, ginger, and turmeric and sauté until they have softened, about 3 minutes.

Add the liquid. Mix in the coconut milk, lime juice then bring the mixture to a boil.

Steam the mussels. Put the mussels to the skillet, cover, and steam until the shells are open, about 10 minutes. Take the skillet off the heat and throw out any unopened mussels.

Add the herbs. Stir in the scallion, cilantro, and thyme.

Serve. Divide the mussels and the sauce into 4 bowls and serve them immediately.

Nutrition:

Calories: 319

Total fat: 23g

Total carbs: 8g

Fiber: 2g;

Net carbs: 6g

Sodium: 395mg

Protein: 23g

Basil Halibut Red Pepper Packets

Preparation Time: 10 minutes

Cooking Time: 20 minutes

Servings: 4

Ingredients:

1. 2 cups cauliflower florets

2. 1 cup roasted red pepper strips

3. ½ cup sliced sun-dried tomatoes

4. 4 (4-ounce) halibut fillets

5. ¼ cup chopped fresh basil

6. Juice of 1 lemon

7. ¼ cup good-quality olive oil

8. Sea salt, for seasoning

9. Freshly ground black pepper, for seasoning

Directions:

- Preheat the oven. Set the oven temperature to 400°F. Cut into four (12-inch) square pieces of aluminum foil. Have a baking sheet ready.

Make the packets. Divide the cauliflower, red pepper strips, and sun-dried tomato between the four pieces of foil, placing the vegetables in the middle of each piece. Top each pile with 1 halibut fillet, and top each fillet with equal amounts of the basil, lemon juice, and olive oil. Fold and crimp the foil to form sealed packets of fish and vegetables and place them on the baking sheet.

Bake. Bake the packets for about 20 minutes, until the fish flakes with a fork. Be careful of the steam when you open the packet!

Serve. Transfer the vegetables and halibut to four plates, season with salt and pepper, and serve immediately.

Nutrition:

Calories: 294

Total fat: 18g

Total carbs: 8g

Fiber: 3g

Net carbs: 5g

Sodium: 114mg

Protein: 25g

Sherry and Butter Prawns

Preparation Time: 5 minutes

Cooking Time: 5 minutes

Servings: 4

Ingredients:

1. 1 ½ pounds king prawns, peeled and deveined
2. 2 tablespoons dry sherry
3. 1 teaspoon dried basil
4. 1/2 teaspoon mustard seeds
5. 1 ½ tablespoons fresh lemon juice
6. 1 teaspoon cayenne pepper, crushed
7. 1 tablespoon garlic paste
8. 1/2 stick butter, at room temperature

Directions:

- Whisk the dry sherry with cayenne pepper, garlic paste, basil, mustard seeds, lemon juice and prawns. Let it marinate for 1 hour in your refrigerator.

- In a frying pan, melt the butter over medium-high flame, basting with the reserved marinade.
- Sprinkle with salt and pepper to taste.

Nutrition:

294 Calories

14.3g Fat

3.6g Carbs

34.6g Protein

1.4g Fiber

Clams with Garlic-Tomato Sauce

Preparation Time: 5 minutes

Cooking Time: 20 minutes

Servings: 4

Ingredients:

1. 40 littleneck clams

2. For the Sauce:

3. 2 tomatoes, pureed

4. 2 tablespoons olive oil

5. 1 shallot, chopped

6. Sea salt, to taste

7. Freshly ground black pepper, to taste

8. 1/2 teaspoon paprika

9. 1/3 cup port wine

10.   2 garlic cloves, pressed

11.   1/2 lemon, cut into wedges

Directions:

- Grill the clams until they are open, for 5 to 6 minutes.

- In a frying pan, heat the olive oil over moderate heat. Cook the shallot and garlic until tender and fragrant.
- Stir in the pureed tomatoes, salt, black pepper and paprika and continue to cook an additional 10 to 12 minutes, up to well cooked.
- Heat off and add in the port wine; stir to combine. Garnish with fresh lemon wedges.

Nutrition:

134 Calories

7.8g Fat

5.9g Carbs

8.3g Protein

1g Fiber

Amberjack Fillets with Cheese Sauce

Preparation Time: 10 minutes

Cooking Time: 10 minutes

Servings: 4

Ingredients:

1. 6 amberjack fillets
2. 1/4 cup fresh tarragon chopped
3. 2 tablespoons olive oil, at room temperature
4. Sea salt, to taste
5. Ground black pepper, to taste
6. For the Sauce:
7. 1/3 cup vegetable broth
8. 3/4 cup double cream
9. 1/3 cup Romano cheese, grated
10. 3 teaspoons butter, at room temperature
11. 2 garlic cloves, finely minced

Directions:

- In a non-stick frying pan, warm the olive oil until sizzling.
- Once hot, fry the amberjack for about 6 minutes per side or until the edges are turning opaque. Sprinkle them with salt, black pepper, and tarragon. Reserve.
- To make the sauce, melt the butter in a saucepan over moderately high heat. Sauté the garlic until tender and fragrant or about 2 minutes.
- Add in the vegetable broth and cream and continue to cook for 5 to 6 minutes more; heat off.
- Stir in the Romano cheese and continue stirring in the residual heat for a couple of minutes more.

Nutrition:

285 Calories

20.4g Fat

1.2g Carbs

23.8g Protein,0.1g Fiber

Tilapia with Spicy Dijon Sauce

Preparation Time: 10 minutes

Cooking Time: 5 minutes

Servings: 4

Ingredients:

1. 1 tablespoon butter, room temperature
2. 2 chili peppers, deveined and minced
3. 1 cup heavy cream
4. 1 teaspoon Dijon mustard
5. 1 pound tilapia fish, cubed
6. Sea salt, to taste
7. Ground black pepper, to taste
8. 1 cup white onions, chopped
9. 1 teaspoon garlic, pressed
10. 1/2 cup dark rum

Directions:

- Toss the tilapia with salt, pepper, onions, garlic, chili peppers and rum. Let it marinate for 2 hours in your refrigerator.

- In a grill pan, melt the butter over a moderately high heat. Sear the fish in hot butter, basting with the reserved marinade.
- Add in the mustard and cream and continue to cook until everything is thoroughly cooked, for 2 to 3 minutes.

Nutrition:

228 Calories

13g Fat

6.5g Carbs

13.7g Protein

1.1g Fiber

Garlic Butter Shrimps

Preparation Time: 13 minutes

Cooking Time: 16 minutes

Servings: 3

Ingredients:

- ½ pound shrimp, peeled and deveined
- 2 garlic cloves
- ½ white onion
- 3 tbsp. ghee butter
- 1 tsp black pepper
- 1 lemon (peeled)
- Himalayan rock salt to taste

Directions:

1. Preheat the oven to 425F
2. Mince the garlic and onion, cut the lemon in half
3. Season the shrimps with pink salt and pepper
4. Slice one-half of the lemon thinly, cut the other half into 2 pieces

5. Grease a baking dish with the butter; combine the shrimp with the garlic, onion and lemon slices, put in the baking dish

6. Bake the shrimps for 15 minutes, stirring halfway through

7. Remove the shrimps from the oven and squeeze the juice from 2 lemon pieces over the dish

Nutrition:

Carbs: 3, 9 g

Fat: 19, 8 g

Protein: 32 g

Calories: 338

Oven-Baked Sole Fillets

Preparation Time: 10 minutes

Cooking Time: 20 minutes

Servings: 4

Ingredients:

1. 2 tablespoons olive oil

2. 1/2 tablespoon Dijon mustard

3. 1 teaspoon garlic paste

4. 1/2 tablespoon fresh ginger, minced

5. 1/2 teaspoon porcini powder

6. Salt and ground black pepper, to taste

7. 1/2 teaspoon paprika

8. 4 sole fillets

9. 1/4 cup fresh parsley, chopped

Directions:

- Combine the oil, Dijon mustard, garlic paste, ginger, porcini powder, salt, black pepper, and paprika.

- Rub this mixture all over sole fillets. Place the sole fillets in a lightly oiled baking pan.

- Bake in the preheated oven at 400 degrees F for about 20 minutes.

Nutrition:

195 Calories

8.2g Fat

0.5g Carbs

28.7g Protein, 0.6g Fiber

Keto Zoodles with White Clam Sauce

Preparation Time: 10 minutes

Cooking Time: 10 minutes

Servings: 4

Ingredients:

1. 2 pounds small clams
2. 8 cups zucchini noodles
3. 1/2 cup dry white wine
4. 1/4 cup butter
5. 1/4 cup fresh parsley (chopped)
6. 2 tablespoons lemon juice
7. 2 tablespoons olive oil
8. 1 tablespoon garlic (minced)
9. 1 teaspoon kosher salt
10. 1 teaspoon lemon zest (grated)
11. 1/4 teaspoon black pepper (ground)

Directions:

- In a pan at medium heat, place the olive oil, butter, pepper, and salt. Stir to melt the butter.
- Put in the garlic. Sautee the garlic until fragrant for at least 2 minutes
- Set in the lemon juice and wine. Cook for at least 2 minutes, until the liquid is slightly reduced
- Put in the clams. Cook the clams until they are all opened (about 3 minutes). Discard any clam that does not open after 3 minutes.
- Remove the pan from the heat. Put in the zucchini noodles. Toss the mixture to combine well. Let the zoodles rest for a couple of minutes to soften them.
- Put in the lemon zest and parsley. Stir. Serve.

Nutrition:

Calories: 311

Carbs: 9 g

Fats: 19 g

Proteins: 13 g

Fiber: 2 g

Fried Codfish with Almonds

Preparation Time: 8 minutes

Cooking Time: 18 minutes

Servings: 3

Ingredients:

- 16 oz. codfish fillet
- 3 oz. chopped almonds
- ½ tsp chili pepper
- 1 egg
- 1 tbsp. ghee butter
- 1 tsp psyllium
- 3 oz. cream
- 3 tbsp. keto mayo
- 1 tbsp. chopped fresh dill
- 1 tsp minced garlic
- ½ tsp onion powder
- Salt and pepper to taste

Directions:

1. In a small mixing bowl, combine the psyllium, onion powder, chili, and almonds

2. Beat the eggs in another bowl, mix well

3. Warm the butter in a skillet at medium heat.

4. Cut the fillet into 3 slices

5. Dip into the egg mixture, then into almonds and spices

6. Fry in the skillet for about 7 minutes each side

7. Meanwhile, in another bowl combine the cream, garlic, dill, and salt, stir well

8. Serve the fish with this sauce

Nutrition:

Carbs: 4, 9 g

Fats: 63 g

Protein: 33, 6 g

Calories: 709

Salmon Balls

Preparation Time: 5 minutes

Cooking Time: 13 minutes

Servings: 2

Ingredients:

- 1 can of tuna
- 2 tbsp. keto mayo
- 1 avocado
- 1 egg
- 1 garlic clove
- ½ cup heavy cream
- 3 tbsp. coconut oil
- ½ tsp ginger powder
- ½ tsp paprika
- ½ tsp dried cilantro
- 2 tbsp. lemon juice
- 2 tbsp. water
- Salt and ground black pepper to taste

Directions:

1. Drain the salmon, chop it

2. Mince the garlic clove, peel the avocado
3. In a bowl, combine the fish, mayo, egg, and garlic, season with salt, paprika, and ginger, mix well
4. Make 4 balls of it
5. Warm the oil in a skillet at medium heat
6. Put the balls and fry for 4-6 minutes each side
7. Meanwhile, put the heavy cream, avocado, cilantro, lemon juice, and 1 tablespoon of oil in a blender. Pulse well
8. Serve the balls with the sauce

Nutrition:

Carbs: 3,9 g

Fats: 50 g

Protein: 20,1 g

Calories: 555

Codfish Sticks

Preparation Time: 8 minutes

Cooking Time: 15 minutes

Servings: 2

Ingredients:

- 9 oz. codfish fillet
- 2 eggs
- 2 tbsp. ghee butter
- 2 tbsp. coconut flour
- ½ tsp paprika
- Salt and pepper to taste

Directions:

1. Slice the fish into sticks
2. In a bowl, put and mix the eggs, flour, paprika, pepper, and salt
3. Warm the butter in a skillet at medium heat.
4. Dip each fish slice into the spice mixture
5. Fry in the skillet over low heat for 4-5 minutes per side

Nutrition:

Carbs: 1,5 g

Fat: 31 g

Protein: 22,5 g

Calories: 329

Shrimp Risotto

Preparation Time: 10 minutes

Cooking Time: 15 minutes

Servings: 4

Ingredients:

- 14 oz. shrimps, peeled and deveined
- 12 oz. cauli rice
- 4 button mushrooms
- ½ lemon
- 4 stalks green onion
- 3 tbsp. ghee butter
- 2 tbsp. coconut oil
- Salt and black pepper to taste

Directions:

1. Preheat the oven to 400F
2. Put a layer of cauli rice on a sheet pan, season with salt and spices; sprinkle the coconut oil over it
3. Bake in the oven for 10-12 minutes

4. Cut the green onion, slice up the mushrooms and remove the rind from the lemon
5. Heat the ghee butter in a skillet over medium heat. Add the shrimps; season it and sauté for 5-6 minutes
6. Top the cauli rice with the shrimps, sprinkle the green onion over it

Nutrition:

Carbs: 9,2 g

Fat: 26,2 g

Protein: 25 g

Calories: 363

Lemony Trout

Preparation Time: 10 minutes

Cooking Time: 20 minutes

Servings: 2

Ingredients:

- 5 tbsp. ghee butter
- 5 oz. trout fillets
- 2 garlic cloves
- 1 tsp rosemary
- 1 lemon
- 2 tbsp. capers
- Salt and pepper to taste

Directions:

1. Preheat the oven to 400F
2. Peel the lemon, mince the garlic cloves and chop the capers
3. Season the trout fillets with salt, rosemary, and pepper
4. Grease a baking dish with the oil and place the fish onto it

5. Warm the butter in a skillet over medium heat

6. Add the garlic and cook for 4-5 minutes until golden

7. Remove from the heat, add the lemon zest and 2 tablespoons of lemon juice, stir well

8. Pour the lemon-butter sauce over the fish and top with the capers

9. Bake for 14-15 minutes. Serve hot

Nutrition:

Carbs: 3,1 g

Fat: 25 g

Protein: 15,8 g

Calories: 302

Quick Fish Bowl

Preparation Time: 11 minutes

Cooking Time: 15 minutes

Servings: 2

Ingredients:

- 2 tilapia fillets
- 1 tbsp. olive oil
- 1 avocado
- 1 tbsp. ghee butter
- 1 tbsp. cumin powder
- 1 tbsp. paprika
- 2 cups coleslaw cabbage, chopped
- 1 tbsp. salsa sauce
- Himalayan rock salt, to taste
- Black pepper to taste

Directions:

1. Preheat the oven to 425F. Line a baking sheet with the foil
2. Mash the avocado

3. Brush the tilapia fillets using olive oil, season with salt and spices

4. Place the fish onto the baking sheet, greased with the ghee butter

5. Bake for 15 minutes, then remove the fish from the heat and let it cool for 5 minutes

6. In a bowl, combine the coleslaw cabbage and the salsa sauce, toss gently

7. Add the mashed avocado, season with salt and pepper

8. Slice the fish and add to the bowl

9. Bake for 14-15 minutes. Serve hot

Nutrition:

Carbs: 5,2 g

Fat: 24,5 g

Protein: 16,1 g

Calories: 321

Tender Creamy Scallops

Preparation Time: 15 minutes

Cooking Time: 21 minutes

Servings: 2

Ingredients:

- 8 fresh sea scallops
- 4 bacon slices
- ½ cup grated parmesan cheese
- 1 cup heavy cream
- 2 tbsp. ghee butter
- Salt and black pepper to taste

Directions:

1. Heat the butter in a skillet at medium-high heat
2. Add the bacon and cook for 4-5 minutes each side (till crispy)
3. Moved to a paper towel to remove the excess fat
4. Lower the heat to medium, sprinkle with more butter. Put the heavy cream and

parmesan cheese, season with salt and pepper

5. Reduce the heat to low and cook for 8-10 minutes, constantly stirring, until the sauce thickens

6. In another skillet, heat the ghee butter over medium-high heat

7. Add the scallops to the skillet, season with salt and pepper. Cook for 2 minutes per side until golden

8. Transfer the scallops to a paper towel

9. Top with the sauce and crumbled bacon

Nutrition:

Carbs: 11 g

Fat: 72,5 g

Protein: 24 g

Calories: 765

Salmon Cakes

Preparation Time: 10 minutes

Cooking Time: 10 minutes

Servings: 2

Ingredients:

- 6 oz. canned salmon
- 1 large egg
- 2 tbsp. pork rinds
- 3 tbsp. keto mayo
- 1 tbsp. ghee butter
- 1 tbsp. Dijon mustard
- Salt and ground black pepper to taste

Directions:

1. In a bowl, combine the salmon (drained), pork rinds, egg, and half of the mayo, season with salt and pepper. Mix well
2. With the salmon mixture, form the cakes
3. Heat the ghee butter in a skillet over medium-high heat

4. Place the salmon cakes in the skillet and cook for about 3 minutes per side. Moved to a paper towel to get rid of excess fat
5. In a small bowl, combine the remaining half of mayo and the Dijon mustard, mix well
6. Serve the salmon cakes with the mayo-mustard sauce

Nutrition:

Carbs: 1,2 g

Fat: 31 g

Protein: 24,2 g

Calories: 370

Salmon with Mustard Cream

Preparation Time: 10 minutes

Cooking Time: 12 minutes

Servings: 2

Ingredients:

1. 2 salmon fillets

2. ¼ cup keto mayo

3. 1 tbsp. Dijon mustard

4. 2 tbsp. fresh cilantro, minced

5. 2 tbsp. ghee butter

6. ½ tsp garlic powder

- Salt and pepper to taste

Directions:

- Preheat the oven to 450F. Grease a baking dish with the ghee butter

- Season the salmon with salt and pepper and put in the baking dish

- In a mixing bowl, put and combine the Dijon mustard, mayo, parsley, and garlic powder. Stir well

- Top the salmon fillets with the mustard sauce
- Bake for 10 minutes

Nutrition:

Carbs: 2 g

Fat: 41,5 g

Protein: 32,9 g

Calories: 505

Shrimp and Black Beans Enchalada

Preparation Time: 5 minutes

Cooking Time: 15 minutes

Servings: 4

Ingredients:

- 2 cans (10 g) of red or green enchilada sauce
- 1 lb. shrimp
- 2 cans (15 oz.) black beans
- 2 cups grated Mexican cheese mixture
- 12 to 13 small flour tortillas

Directions:

1. Preheat the oven to 400° F. Put ¼ cup sauce (enchiladas) in a saucepan. Increase the heat and add the shrimp. Cook until the shrimp are clean and no longer transparent for about 5 minutes. Remove from the heated container.

2. Place the enchiladas in a 9 x 13-inch baking dish. Organize a pea breakfast, 3 or 4 shrimp, and a slice of cheese on an omelet. Fold the tortilla edges into the oven dish on the filling and with the seam facing down.

3. Repeat with the remaining tortillas. Pour out the rest of the enchilada sauce after preparing all the enchiladas.

4. Bake until all the cheese has melted for 15 minutes.

Nutrition:

Calories: 196

Fat: 12g

Net Carbs: 4g

Protein: 17g

Tuna Steaks with Shirataki Noodles

Preparation Time: 10 minutes

Cooking Time: 20 minutes

Servings: 4

Ingredients:

- 1 pack (7 oz.) miracle noodle angel hair
- 3 cups water
- 1 red bell pepper, seeded and halved
- 4 tuna steaks
- Salt and black pepper to taste
- Olive oil for brushing
- 2 tablespoons pickled ginger
- 2 tablespoons chopped cilantro

Directions:

1. Cook the shirataki rice based on the package instructions: In a colander, rinse the shirataki noodles with running cold water.
2. Place a pot of salted water to a boil; blanch the noodles for 2 minutes.

3. Drain and moved to a dry skillet over medium heat.

4. Dry roast for a few minutes until opaque.

5. Grease a grill's grate using a cooking spray and preheat on medium heat. Spice the red bell pepper and tuna with salt and black pepper, brush with olive oil, and grill covered.

6. Cook both for at least 3 minutes on each side. Moved to a plate to cool. Dice bell pepper with a knife.

7. Arrange the noodles, tuna, and bell pepper into the serving plate.

8. Top with pickled ginger and garnish with cilantro.

9. Serve with roasted sesame sauce.

Nutrition:

Calories: 310

Fat: 18.2g

Net Carbs: 2g

Protein: 22g

Tilapia with Parmesan Bark

Preparation Time: 4 minutes

Cooking Time: 12 minutes

Servings: 4

Ingredients:

- ¾ cup freshly grated Parmesan cheese

- 2 teaspoons pepper

- 1 tablespoon chopped parsley

- 4 tilapia fillets (4 us)
- Lemon cut into pieces

Directions:

1. Set the oven to 400° F. Mix cheese in a shallow dish with pepper and parsley and season with salt and pepper.
2. Mix the fish in the cheese with olive oil and flirt. Place on a baking sheet with foil and bake for 10 to 12 minutes until the fish in the thickest part is opaque.
3. Serve the lemon slices with the fish.

Nutrition:

Calories: 210

Fat: 9.3g

Net Carbs: 1.3g

Protein: 28.9g

Blackened Fish Tacos with Slaw:

Preparation Time: 14 minutes

Cooking Time: 6 minutes

Servings: 4

Ingredients:

- 1 tablespoon olive oil

- 1 teaspoon chili powder

- 2 tilapia fillets

- 1 teaspoon paprika

- 4 low carb tortillas

Slaw:

1. ½ cup red cabbage, shredded

2. 1 tablespoon lemon juice

3. 1 teaspoon apple cider vinegar

4. 1 tablespoon olive oil

5. Salt and black pepper to taste

Directions:

- Season the tilapia with chili powder and paprika. Heat the vegetable oil during a skillet over medium heat.

- Add tilapia and cook until blackened, about 3 minutes per side. Cut into strips. Divide the tilapia between the tortillas. Blend all the slaw ingredients in a bowl and top the fish to serve.

Nutrition:

Calories: 268

Fat: 20g

Net Carbs: 3.5g

Protein: 13.8g

Mozzarella Fish

Preparation Time: 5 minutes

Cooking Time: 10-15 minutes

Servings: 6-8

Ingredients:

1. 2 lbs. of bone gold sole

2. Salt and pepper to taste

3. ½ teaspoon dried oregano

4. 1 cup grated mozzarella cheese

5. 1 large fresh tomato, sliced thinly

Directions:

- Excellent source of cooking the butter. Organize a single layer of trout. Add salt, pepper, and oregano.

- Top with sliced cheese slices and tomatoes.

- Cook, covered, for 10 to 15 minutes at 425°F.

Nutrition:

Calories: 156

Fat: 6g ,Net Carbs: 5g, Protein: 8g

Popcorn Shrimp

Preparation Time: 5 minutes

Cooking Time: 20 minutes

Servings: 2

Ingredients:

1. 1/2 lb. (225 g) small shrimp, peeled
2. 2 eggs, whisked
3. 6 Tablespoons (36 g) cajun seasoning
4. 6 Tablespoons (42 g) coconut flour
5. Coconut oil for frying

Directions:

- Warm the coconut oil in a saucepan (use enough coconut oil so that it's 1/2 inch (1-2 cm) deep) or deep fryer.
- Place the whisked eggs into a large bowl, and in another large bowl, combine the coconut flour and seasoning.
- Toss a handful of the shrimp into the whisked eggs and stir around so that each shrimp is coated.

- Then take the shrimp out of the whisked eggs the put into the seasoning bowl. Coat the shrimp using the coconut flour and seasoning mixture.
- Bring the coated shrimp into the hot oil and fry until golden. (Don't stir the pot and the shrimp must in deep-fried)
- Using a slotted spoon, take off the shrimp and place on paper towels to absorb the excess oil. Repeat for the remaining shrimp (change the oil if there are too many solids in it).
- Cool for at least 10 minutes.

Nutrition:

Calories: 390

Fat: 23 g

Net Carbohydrates: 3 g

Protein: 30 g

Cucumber Ginger Shrimp

Preparation Time: 5 minutes

Cooking Time: 10 minutes

Servings: 1

Ingredients:

1. 1 large cucumber, sliced into 1/2-inch round
2. 10-15 large shrimp/prawns
3. 1 teaspoon (1 g) fresh ginger, grated
4. Salt to taste
5. Coconut oil to cook with

Directions:

- Pour 1 Tablespoon (15 ml) of coconut oil into a frying pan on medium heat.
- Put the ginger and the cucumber and sauté for 2-3 minutes.
- Add in the shrimp then cook until they turn pink and are no longer translucent.
- Add salt to taste and serve.

Nutrition: Calories: 250,Fat: 16 g, Net Carbohydrates: 4 g,Protein: 20 g

Salmon with Pesto

Preparation Time: 10 minutes

Cooking Time: 15 minutes

Servings: 4

Ingredients:

1. 4 salmon fillets

2. 2 teaspoons olive oil

3. Pinch of salt

4. ½-cup pesto

Directions:

- Arrange the greased Cook & Crisp Basket in the pot of Ninja Foodi.

- Close the Ninja Foodi with crisping lid and select Air Crisp.

- Set the temperature to 270 degrees F for 5 minutes.

- Press Start/Stop to begin preheating.

- Drizzle the salmon fillets with oil evenly and sprinkle with a pinch of salt.

- After preheating, open the lid.

- Place the salmon fillets into the Cook & Crisp Basket.
- Close the Ninja Foodi with crisping lid and select Air Crisp.
- Set the temperature to 270 degrees F for 20 minutes.
- Press Start/Stop to begin cooking.
- Transfer the salmon fillets onto a platter and top with the pesto.
- Serve immediately.

Nutrition:

Calories: 380

Fats: 25.8g

Carbohydrates: 2g

Proteins: 36g

Salmon in Dill Sauce

Preparation Time: 10 minutes

Cooking Time: 2 hours

Servings: 6

Ingredients:

1. 2 cups water

2. 1-cup homemade chicken broth

3. 2 tablespoons fresh lemon juice

4. ¼ cup fresh dill, chopped

5. 6 salmon fillets

6. 1 teaspoon cayenne pepper

7. Salt and ground black pepper

Directions:

- In the pot of Ninja Foodi, mix together the water, broth, lemon juice, lemon juice and dill.

- Organize the salmon fillets on top, skin side down, and sprinkle with cayenne pepper, salt black pepper.

- Close the Ninja Foodi with crisping lid and select Slow Cooker.
- Set on Low for 1-2 hours.
- Press Start/Stop to begin cooking.
- Serve hot.

Nutrition:

Calories: 164

Fats: 7.4g

Carbohydrates 1.6 g

Proteins: 23.3g

Seasoned Catfish

Preparation Time: 15 minutes

Cooking Time: 23 minutes

Servings: 4

Ingredients:

1. 4 catfish fillets

2. 2 tablespoons Italian seasoning

3. Salt and ground black pepper

4. 1 tablespoon olive oil

5. 1 tablespoon fresh parsley, chopped

Directions:

- Arrange the greased Cook & Crisp Basket in the pot of Ninja Foodi.

- Close the Ninja Foodi with crisping lid and select Air Crisp.

- Set the temperature to 400 °F for 5 minutes.

- Press Start/Stop to begin preheating.

- Rub the fish fillets with seasoning, salt, and black pepper generously and then coat with oil.
- After preheating, open the lid.
- Place the catfish fillets into the Cook & Crisp Basket.
- Close the Ninja Foodi with crisping lid and select Air Crisp.
- Set the temperature to 400°F for 20 minutes.
- Press Start/Stop to begin cooking.
- Flip the fish fillets once halfway through.
- Serve hot with the garnishing of parsley.

Nutrition:

Calories: 205

Fats: 14.2g

Carbohydrates 0.8 g

Proteins: 17.7g

Parsley Tilapia

Preparation Time: 15 minutes

Cooking Time: 1 hour and 30 minutes

Servings: 6

Ingredients:

1. 6 tilapia fillets

2. Salt and ground black pepper

3. ½ cup yellow onion, chopped

4. 3 teaspoons fresh lemon rind, grated finely

5. ¼ cup fresh parsley, chopped

6. 2 tablespoon unsalted butter, melted

Directions:

- Grease the pot of Ninja Foodi.

- Spice the tilapia fillets with salt and black pepper generously.

- In the prepared pot of Ninja Foodi, place the tilapia fillets.

- Arrange the onion, lemon rind, and parsley over fillets evenly and drizzle with melted butter.

- Close the Ninja Foodi with crisping lid and select Slow Cooker.

- Set on Low for 1½ hours.

- Press Start/Stop to begin cooking.

- Serve hot.

Nutrition:

Calories: 133

Fats: 4.9g

Carbohydrates: 1.3g

Proteins: 21.3g

Crispy Tilapia

Preparation Time: 15 minutes

Cooking Time: 14 minutes

Servings: 4

Ingredients:

1. ¾ cup pork rinds, crushed

2. 1 packet dry ranch-style dressing mix

3. 2½ tablespoons olive oil

4. 2 organic eggs

5. 4 tilapia fillets

Directions:

- Arrange the greased Cook & Crisp Basket in the pot of Ninja Foodi.

- Close the Ninja Foodi with crisping lid and select Air Crisp.

- Set the temperature to 355 degrees F for 5 minutes.

- Press "Start/Stop" to begin preheating.

- In a shallow bowl, beat the eggs.

- In another bowl, add the pork rinds, ranch dressing, and oil and mix until a crumbly mixture form.
- Put the fish fillets into the egg then coat with the pork rind mixture.
- After preheating, open the lid.
- Arrange the tilapia fillets in the prepared Cook & Crisp Basket in a single layer.
- Close the Ninja Foodi with crisping lid and select Air Crisp.
- Set the temperature to 350°F for 14 minutes.
- Press Start/Stop to begin cooking.
- Serve hot.

Nutrition:

Calories: 304

Fats: 16.8g

Carbohydrates 0.4 g

Proteins: 38g

Cod with Tomatoes

Preparation Time: 15 minutes

Cooking Time: 16 minutes

Servings: 4

Ingredients:

1. 1-pound cherry tomatoes halved

2. 2 tablespoons fresh rosemary, chopped

3. 4 cod fillets

4. 2 garlic cloves, minced

5. 1 tablespoon olive oil

6. Salt and ground black pepper

Directions:

- At the bottom of a greased a large heatproof bowl, place half of the cherry tomatoes followed by the rosemary.

- Arrange cod fillets on top in a single layer, followed by the remaining tomatoes.

- Sprinkle with garlic and drizzle with oil.

- At the bottom of Ninja Foodie, arrange the bowl.

- Close the Ninja Foodi with the pressure lid and place the pressure valve to Seal position.
- Select Pressure and set to High for 6 minutes.
- Press Start/Stop to begin cooking.
- Switch the valve to Vent and do a quick release.
- Transfer the fish fillets and tomatoes onto serving plates.
- Sprinkle with salt and black pepper and serve.

Nutrition:

Calories: 149

Fats: 5g

Carbohydrates 6 g

Proteins: 21.4g

Crab Casserole

Preparation Time: 10 minutes

Cooking Time: 30 minutes

Servings: 5

Ingredients:

1. 2 tbsp. of oil, for frying

2. 1 onion, finely chopped

3. 150 g finely chopped celery stalks

4. salt and pepper

5. 300 ml homemade mayonnaise

6. 4 eggs

7. 450 g canned crab meat

8. 325 g grated white cheddar cheese

9. 2 tsp. paprika

10.   ¼ tsp. cayenne pepper

11.   For filing

12.   75 g leafy greens

13.   2 tbsp. of olive oil

Directions:

- Set the oven to 350°F. Grease a 9x12 baking dish.
- Fry onion and celery in oil until translucent.
- In another bowl, add mayonnaise, eggs, crab meat, seasonings, and ⅔ chopped cheese. Add the fried onions and celery and stir.
- Add the mass to the baking dish. Sprinkle the remaining cheese on top and bake for about 30 minutes or until golden brown.
- Serve with salad and olive oil.

Nutrition:

Carbohydrates: 6 g

Fats: 95 g

Proteins: 47 g

Calories: 400

Cod with Bell Pepper

Preparation Time: 15 minutes

Cooking Time: 1 hour and 30 minutes

Servings: 4

Ingredients:

1. 1 bell pepper, seeded and sliced

2. ½ small onion, sliced

3. 3 garlic cloves, minced

4. 1 can sugar-free diced tomatoes

5. 1 tablespoon fresh rosemary, chopped

6. ¼ cup homemade fish broth

7. ¼ teaspoon red pepper flakes

8. Salt and ground black pepper

9. 1-pound cod fillets

Directions:

- In the pot of Ninja Foodi, add all the ingredients except cod and stir to combine.

- Season cod fillets with salt and black pepper evenly.

- Arrange the cod fillets over broth mixture.

- Close the Ninja Foodi with crisping lid and select Slow Cooker.
- Set on High for 1½ hours.
- Press Start/Stop to begin cooking.
- Serve hot.

Nutrition:

Calories: 129

Fats: 1.6g

Carbohydrates 7.7 g

Proteins: 22.1g

Salmon Skewers in Cured Ham

Preparation Time: 10 minutes

Cooking Time: 15 minutes

Servings: 4

Ingredients:

1. Salmon Skewers

2. 60 ml finely chopped fresh basil

3. 450 g salmon

4. salt black pepper

5. 100 g dried ham sliced

6. 1 tbsp. l Olive oil

7. 8 pcs wooden skewers

8. Innings

9. 225 ml mayonnaise

Directions:

- Soak the skewers in water.

- Finely chop fresh basil.

- Cut salmon fillet into rectangular pieces and fasten on skewers.

- Roll each kebab in the basil and pepper.

- Cut the cured ham into thin slices and wrap her every kebab.

- Lubricate with olive oil and fry on in a pan, grill, or in the oven.

- Serve with mayonnaise or salad

Nutrition:

Carbohydrates: 1 g

Fats: 62 g

Proteins: 28 g

Calories: 680

Fish Casserole with Cream Cheese Sauce

Preparation Time: 10 minutes

Cooking Time: 35 minutes

Servings: 4

Ingredients:

1. 280 g broccoli
2. 280 g cooked fish
3. 85 g grated Gouda cheese
4. 1 tsp. chopped green onions
5. 1 liter of water
6. For the sauce:
7. 119 ml of fat cream
8. 2 tbsp. grated Parmesan cheese
9. 1 tbsp. butter
10. 56.7 g cream cheese
11. 1/4 tsp. chopped garlic
12. 1/8 tsp. Chile
13. Sea salt and black pepper to taste

Directions:

- Preheat the oven to 350° F.
- Set all the sauce ingredients into a saucepan and simmer for 3 minutes, stirring occasionally.
- In another saucepan, bring the water to a boil and cook the broccoli for 3 minutes or until tender.
- Mash the fish with a fork.
- Put the broccoli in a casserole dish, put the chopped fish on top, pour the sauce and sprinkle with grated cheese.
- Bake for at least 20 minutes or until golden brown.
- Let stand for 5 minutes, sprinkle with chopped green onions and enjoy!

Nutrition:

Carbohydrates: 9 g

Fats: 36 g

Proteins: 32 g

Calories: 474

Bacon and Jalapeno Wrapped Shrimp

Preparation Time: 10 minutes

Cooking Time: 20 minutes

Servings: 2

Ingredients:

1. 4 jalapeño peppers, seedless and cut into 3 to 4 long strips each
2. 12 large shrimp, deveined, butterflied, tail-on
3. Salt
4. Freshly ground black pepper
5. 6 thin bacon slices
6. ¼ cup shredded pepper jack cheese

Directions:

- Preheat the oven to 350°F.
- On a baking sheet, arrange the jalapeño strips in a single layer and roast for 10 minutes.

- In a small bowl, season the shrimp with salt and pepper.
- Remove the jalapeño strips from the oven. Place a strip inside each open butterflied shrimp. Wrap each shrimp with bacon and insert it with a toothpick. Organize in a single layer on a baking sheet.
- Cook for 8 minutes until the bacon is crispy.
- Adjust the oven to broil.
- Sprinkle the cheese on top of the shrimp and broil for about 1 minute, until the cheese is bubbling.

Nutrition:

Calories: 240

Total Fat: 16 g

Protein: 21 g

Total Carbs: 3g

Fiber: 1g

Net Carbs: 2g

Crispy Fish Stick

Preparation Time: 10 minutes

Cooking Time: 10 minutes

Servings: 4

Ingredients:

1. 1 cup avocado oil or other cooking oil, plus more as needed
2. 1 pound frozen cod, thawed
3. 2 large eggs
4. 2 tablespoons avocado oil mayonnaise
5. 1 cup almond flour
6. ½ cup grated Parmesan cheese
7. ½ cup ground pork rinds
8. ½ teaspoon chili powder
9. ½ teaspoon chopped fresh parsley
10. Salt
11. Freshly ground black pepper
12. ¼ cup Dairy-Free Tartar Sauce

Directions:

- In a skillet, heat the avocado oil at high heat. You want the oil to be about ½ inch deep, so adjust the amount of oil-based on your pan's size.
- Pat the dry fish using paper towels to remove any excess water.
- In a small bowl, put the eggs and mayonnaise then whisk.
- In another bowl, put the almond flour, Parmesan, pork rinds, chili powder, and parsley and mix well. Season with salt and pepper.
- Cut the cod into strips.
- Put the fish into the egg mixture then dredge in the dry mixture. Press the strips into the dry mixture so that the "breading" sticks well on all sides.
- Add 3 to 4 fish sticks at a time to the hot oil. The oil should sizzle when you put the fish sticks. Cook for at least 2 minutes each side, or until golden and crispy.

- Place the cooked fish sticks on a paper towel-lined plate while you continue to fry the rest of the fish sticks.
- Serve with the tartar sauce.

Nutrition:

Calories: 402

Total Fat: 30g

Protein: 30g

Total Carbs: 3g

Fiber: 1g

Net Carbs: 2g

Prosciutto-Wrapped Cod

Preparation Time: 5 minutes

Cooking Time: 10 minutes

Servings: 2

Ingredients:

1. 2 (6-ounce) cod fillets

2. Freshly ground black pepper

3. 4 prosciutto slices

4. 2 tablespoons butter or ghee

Directions:

- Pat the dry fish using paper towels to remove any excess water.

- Season the fillets with pepper and wrap the prosciutto around the fillets.

- Heat a skillet at medium heat then add the butter.

- Once the pan is hot, add the fillets and cook on each side for 5 minutes, up to the outside is crispy and the inside is flaky.

- Place the cooked fish onto a paper towel-lined plate to absorb any excess oil.

Nutrition:

Calories: 317

Total Fat: 18g

Protein: 38g

Total Carbs: 0g

Fiber: 0g

Net Carbs: 0g

Coconut Mahi-Mahi Nuggets

Preparation Time: 10 minutes

Cooking Time: 10 minutes

Servings: 2

Ingredients:

1. 1 cup avocado oil or coconut oil, plus more as needed

2. 1 pound frozen mahi-mahi, thawed

3. 2 large eggs

4. 2 tablespoons avocado oil mayonnaise

5. 1 cup almond flour

6. ½ cup shredded coconut

7. ¼ cup crushed macadamia nuts

8. Salt

9. Freshly ground black pepper

10.   ½ lime, cut into wedges

11.   ¼ cup Dairy-Free Tartar Sauce

Directions:

- In a skillet, warm the avocado oil at high heat. You want the oil to be about ½ inch deep, so adjust the amount of oil-based on the size of your pan.

- Pat the fish to try using paper towels to take off any excess water.

- In a small bowl, put and combine the eggs and mayonnaise.

- In a medium mixing bowl, put and combine the almond flour, coconut, and macadamia nuts. Season with salt and pepper. Cut the mahi-mahi into nuggets.

- Put the fish into the egg mixture then dredge in the dry mix. Press into the dry mixture so that "breading" sticks well on all sides.
- Add the fish into the hot oil. It should sizzle when you add the nuggets. Cook for 2 minutes per side, until golden and crispy.
- Place the cooked nuggets on a paper towel-lined plate and squirt the lime wedges over them.

Nutrition:

Calories: 733

Total Fat: 53g

Protein: 54g

Total Carbs: 10g

Fiber: 6g

Net Carbs: 4g

Garlic Crab Legs

Preparation Time: 10 minutes

Cooking Time: 20 minutes

Servings: 2

Ingredients:

1. 4 tablespoons butter or ghee

2. 2 tablespoons extra-virgin olive oil

3. ½ lemon, juiced and zested

4. 4 garlic cloves, crushed and minced

5. 2 teaspoons Old Bay Seasoning

6. 1 tablespoon red pepper flakes

7. 2 pounds crab legs

8. 2 tablespoons chopped fresh parsley

Directions:

- Preheat the oven to 375°F.

- Heat a large oven-safe skillet at medium-low heat. Add the butter, olive oil, lemon juice, lemon zest, garlic, Old Bay, and red pepper flakes. Sauté for 2 minutes.

- Add the crab legs and parsley to the skillet. Spoon the butter mixture over the crab and baste for 3 minutes.
- Bring the skillet in the oven then bake for 15 minutes, basting every 5 minutes.
- Place the crab legs on a platter and pour the butter mixture into a small dish for dipping.

Nutrition:

Calories: 514

Total Fat: 38g

Protein: 41g

Total Carbs: 2g

Fiber: 0g

Net Carbs: 2g

Salmon and Coconut Mix

Preparation Time: 10 minutes

Cooking Time: 20 minutes

Servings: 4

Ingredients:

1. 4 salmon fillets, boneless

2. 3 tbsp. avocado mayonnaise

3. 1 tsp. lime zest, grated

4. ¼ cup coconut cream

5. ¼ cup lime juice

6. ½ cup coconut, unsweetened and shredded

7. 2 tsp. Cajun seasoning

8. A pinch of salt

9. Pinch of black pepper

Directions:

- Set the instant pot on Sauté mode, put the coconut cream and the rest of the ingredients except the fish, mix and cook for at least 5 minutes.

- Add the fish, set the lid on, and cook on High for at least 10 minutes.
- Release the pressure for 10 minutes, divide the salmon and sauce between plates and serve.

Nutrition:

Calories 306

Fat: 17.5

Fiber: 1.4

Carbs: 2.5

Protein: 25.3

Tilapia and Red Sauce

Preparation Time: 10 minutes

Cooking Time: 20 minutes

Servings: 4

Ingredients:

1. 4 tilapia fillets, boneless
2. A pinch of salt and black pepper
3. 2 tablespoons avocado oil
4. 1 tablespoon lemon juice
5. 2 spring onions, minced
6. ½ cup chicken stock
7. ¼ cup tomato passata
8. 1 teaspoon garlic powder
9. 1 teaspoon oregano, dried
10. 1 cup roasted red peppers, chopped
11. 10 ounces canned tomatoes and chilies, chopped

Directions:

- Set the instant pot on Sauté mode, put the oil, heat it up, add the onions, and cook for 2 minutes.
- Put the rest of the ingredients exclude the fish, and simmer everything for 8 minutes more.
- Put the fish, set the lid on, and cook on High for 10 minutes.
- Release the pressure naturally for 10 minutes, divide everything between plates and serve.

Nutrition:

Calories 184

Fat: 2.2

Fiber: 1.6

Carbs: 1.9

Protein: 22.2

Lime Cod Mix

Preparation Time: 10 minutes

Cooking Time: 15 minutes

Servings: 4

Ingredients:

1. 4 cod fillets, boneless
2. ½ teaspoon cumin, ground
3. A pinch of salt and black pepper
4. 1 tablespoon olive oil
5. ½ cup chicken stock
6. 3 tablespoons cilantro, chopped
7. 2 tablespoons lime juice
8. 2 teaspoons lime zest, grated

Directions:

- Set the instant pot on Sauté mode, put oil, heat it, add the cod and cook for 1 minute on each side.
- Add the remaining ingredients, put the lid on, and cook on High for 13 minutes.

- Release the pressure naturally for around 10 minutes, divide the mix between plates and serve.

Nutrition:

Calories 187

Fat: 13.1

Fiber: 0.2

Carbs: 1.6

Protein: 16.1

Salmon and Shrimp Mix

Preparation Time: 5 minutes

Cooking Time: 20 minutes

Servings: 4

Ingredients:

1. 4 salmon fillets, boneless

2. 1 pound shrimp, peeled and deveined

3. 1 teaspoon Cajun seasoning

4. A pinch of salt and black pepper

5. 2 tablespoons olive oil

6. Juice of 1 lemon

7. ½ cup chicken stock

8. 2 tablespoons tomato passata

Directions:

- Set the instant pot on Sauté mode, put the oil, heat it, add the rest of the ingredients except the salmon and shrimp and cook for 3 minutes.

- Add the salmon and cook for 2 minutes on each side.

- Put the shrimp, set the lid on, and cook on High for 10 minutes.

- Release the pressure fast for 5 minutes, divide the mix between plates and serve.

Nutrition:

Calories 393

Fat: 20

Fiber: 0.1

Carbs: 2.2

Protein: 25

Avocado & Salmon Omelet Wrap

Preparation Time: 10 minutes

Cooking Time: 20 minutes

Servings: 2

Ingredients:

1. 3 Large eggs

    a. oz. Smoked salmon

2. .5 of 1 average size Avocado

3. 1 Spring onion

4. 2 tbsp. Cream cheese - full-fat

5. 2 tbsp. Chives - freshly chopped

6. 1 tbsp. Butter or ghee

7. Pepper and salt (as desired)

Directions:

- Add a sprinkle of pepper and salt to the eggs. Use a fork or whisk—mixing them well. Blend in the chives and cream cheese.

- Prepare the salmon and avocado (peel and slice or chop).

- Combine the butter/ghee and the egg mixture in a frying pan. Continue cooking on low heat until done.
- Place the omelet on a serving dish with a portion of cheese over it. Sprinkle the onion, prepared avocado, and salmon into the wrap.
- Close and serve!

Nutrition:

Calories: 765

Net Carbs: 6 g

Total Fat Content: 67 g

Protein: 37 g

Baked Tilapia with Cherry Tomatoes

Preparation Time: 10 minutes

Cooking Time: 25-30 minutes

Servings: 2

Ingredients:

1. 2 tsp. Butter
2. 1-4 oz. Tilapia fillets
3. 8 Cherry tomatoes
4. .25 cup Pitted black olives
5. .5 tsp. Salt
6. .25 tsp. Paprika
7. .25 tsp. Black pepper
8. 1 tsp. Garlic powder
9. 1 tbsp. Freshly squeezed lemon juice
10. 1 tbsp. Optional: Balsamic vinegar

Directions:

- Warm the oven to reach 375º Fahrenheit.
- Grease a roasting pan and add the butter along with the olives and tomatoes.

- Season the tilapia with the spices. Lastly, add the fish fillets into the pan with a spritz of the lemon juice.
- Add a piece of foil over the pan. Bake until the fish easily flakes (25 to 30 min.).
- Garnish with the vinegar if desired.

Nutrition:

Calories: 180

Net Carbs: 4 g

Total Fat Content: 8 g

Protein: 23 g

Garlic & Lemon Shrimp Pasta

Preparation Time: 10 minutes

Cooking Time: 30 minutes

Servings: 4

Ingredients:

1. 2 pkg. Miracle Noodle Angel Hair Pasta

2. 4 Garlic cloves

3. 2 tbsp. Olive oil

4. 2 tbsp. Butter

5. 1 lb. Large raw shrimp

6. .5 of 1 Lemon

7. .5 tsp. Paprika

8. Fresh basil (as desired)

9. Pepper and salt (to taste)

Directions:

- Drain the water from the package of noodles and rinse them in cold water. Toss into a pot of boiling water for two minutes. Transfer to a hot skillet over medium heat to remove

the excess liquid (dry roast). Set them
aside.

- Use the same pan to warm the butter, oil, and mashed garlic. Sauté for a few minutes but don't brown.
- Slice the lemon into rounds and add them to the garlic along with the shrimp. Sauté for approximately three minutes on each side.
- Fold in the noodles and spices and stir to blend the flavors.

Nutrition:

Calories: 360

Net Carbs: 3.5 g

Total Fat Content: 21 g

Protein: 36 g

Sesame Ginger Salmon

Preparation Time: 10 minutes

Cooking Time: 20 minutes

Servings: 2

Ingredients:

1. 1-10 oz. Salmon fillet
2. 1-2 tsp. Minced ginger
3. 2 tbsp. White wine
4. 2 tsp. Sesame oil
5. 1 tbsp. Rice vinegar
6. 2 tbsp. Keto-friendly soy sauce substitute
7. 1 tbsp. Sugar-free ketchup
8. 1 tbsp. Fish sauce – Red Boat

Directions:

- Combine all fixings in a plastic canister with a tight-fitting lid (omit the ketchup, oil, and wine for now). Marinade them for about 1o to 15 minutes.

- On the stovetop, prepare a skillet using the high-heat temperature setting. Pour in the oil. Add the fish when it's hot, skin side down.
- Brown each side for 3-5 minutes.
- Pour in the marinated juices to the pan to simmer when the fish is flipped. Arrange the fish on two dinner plates.
- Pour in the wine and ketchup to the pan and simmer five minutes until it's reduced. Serve with your favorite vegetable.

Nutrition:

Calories: 370

Net Carbs: 2.5 g

Total Fat Content: 24 g

Protein: 33 g

Conclusion

The anti-inflammatory diet cookbook is the perfect resource for anyone who is suffering from inflammation. This cookbook has a special focus on reducing inflammation in the joints, cartilage, and muscles. Each recipe has been carefully developed to help reduce joint pain, joint stiffness, and even autoimmune disorders such as lupus and rheumatoid arthritis.

While most people associate food with comfort, a large number of foods are actually capable of having a dramatic impact on your health. Foods that are high in good fats (omega-3) are especially beneficial for many issues that affect the body. This cookbook provides recipes that are high in good fats and low in inflammatory foods like gluten and dairy. These recipes can be used to help create an anti-inflammatory diet that can help you feel better! The inflammatory disease will lead to many different health consequences and will even attack our most vital organs. The best way to do this is to prevent chronic inflammation in the first place. The next best thing is to recognize the signs and symptoms as early as possible, so proper interventions can be done to limit and reverse the impact of chronic inflammation. Inflammatory disease is the root cause of many long-term diseases, so ignoring the warning signs can create major consequences for your health.

Unfortunately, if the inflammatory disease gets out of control, preventative measures may be out of the question, and medical interventions will need to be done. Our goal is to prevent you from getting to this point. Lucky for us, many lifestyle changes can be performed to stop and reverse this disease process when it is still in its in advance stages. This is another reason why we should recognize and not ignore the signs and symptoms. A major lifestyle change we can commit to is a new diet plan. The anti-inflammatory diet is a meal plan that boasts healthy and nutritious cuisines, but still flavorful and appealing to the taste buds. There is a major myth out there that healthy food cannot be delicious. We have proven this myth wrong by providing numerous recipes from around the world that follow our healthy meal plan.

We hope that the information you read in this book gives you a better understanding of how the immune system functions and how a proper diet plan can help protect it and our other valuable cells and tissues. The recipes we have provided are just a starting point. Use them as a guide to create many of your dishes that follow the diet plan. Just make sure you use the proper ingredients and food groups. Also, for maximum results, follow the Anti-Inflammatory Diet food Guide Pyramid.

The next step is to take the instruction we have provided and begin taking steps to change your life and improve your health. Begin recognizing the signs and symptoms of chronic inflammation and make the necessary lifestyle changes to prevent further health problems. Start transitioning to the anti-inflammatory diet today by incorporating small meals into your schedule and increase the amount as tolerated. Within a short period, the diet will be a regular part of your routine. You will notice increased energy, improved mental function, a stronger and well-balanced immune system, reduction in chronic pain, some healthy weight loss, and overall better health outcomes. If you are ready to experience these changes, then wait no longer and begin putting your knowledge from this book into action.

CPSIA information can be obtained
at www.ICGtesting.com
Printed in the USA
BVHW010806270421
605884BV00022B/150